£2·40

THE BEEZER BOOK

Printed and Published in Great Britain by D. C. Thomson & Co., Ltd.,
185 Fleet Street, London, EC4A 2HS.

A shower of fun with the red-haired one!

THE BADD LADS

BABY CROCKETT

You'll laugh a lot at Pop's robot!

BEEFY DAN
THE FAST-FOOD MAN

Hoss as a bird? Now that's absurd!

I'M STARVING. I'LL LOOK ROUND TOWN FOR SOME GRUB.

Then—

IT'S FEEDING TIME, LITTLE BIRDS.

I'LL HAVE SOME OF THIS BREAD.

But—

BEAT IT, YOU VARMINT. THAT BREAD'S FOR BIRDS, NOT FLEA-BITTEN HORSES!

HM! I'VE GOT AN IDEA. THIS CALLS FOR A POW-WOW WITH MY INDIAN FRIEND.

So—

HOW, FLEET FOOT! CAN YOU DO ME A FAVOUR?

ANYTHING YOU WANT, HOSS.

And soon—

HEE-HEE! I'LL PASS AS A BIRD WITH THESE FEATHERS AND FLIPPERS!

Just take a look at this 'scrap'-book!

SCRAPPER

IT RAINED ALL THROUGH APRIL.

YEAH! AND I 'RAINED' PUNCHES ON BASHER BILL.

BAH! ALL I DID WAS DIG, DIG, DIG IN MAY.

OW!

I GAVE LANKY LANE A GOOD 'DIG' IN THE RIBS.

IT WAS TOO HOT IN JUNE.

WELL, I COOLED A FEW PEOPLE DOWN.

I DID ENJOY GOING FOR A PADDLE IN THE RIVER IN JULY.

I DID A BIT OF 'PADDLING', TOO.

AUGUST WAS A DISASTROUS TIME FOR ME WITH MY CRICKET BAT.

HO-HO! I THINK I WAS A BIG HIT WITH MINE.

EVERYTHING WAS DAMP AND MISERABLE IN SEPTEMBER.

ESPECIALLY TUBBY TATE AFTER I KNOCKED HIM INTO A PUDDLE!

I WASN'T ANY GOOD DUCKING FOR APPLES AT THE HALLOWE'EN PARTY IN OCTOBER.

WHEE! BEEFY BROWN WASN'T MUCH GOOD AT 'DUCKING' EITHER.

PUZZLE

1—This colourfully-dressed gentleman is properly known as a Yeoman of the Guard and can be seen guarding the Crown Jewels in London. Do you know his more familiar nickname? Is it: (a) Beefeater? (b) Grenadier Guard? (c) Royal Archer?

2—Flies beware! This plant actually feeds on small insects. It attracts them with its sweet smell and traps them on its sticky leaves. Is it a: (a) Bee Orchid? (b) Spotted Flycatcher? (c) Sundew?

3—Isn't this a strange creature? About eighteen feet long, it lives in the Arctic Ocean, and its huge tusk is thought to be used for defence. It feeds on squid, fish, prawns and shrimps. Is it a: (a) Porpoise? (b) Killer Whale? (c) Narwhal?

4—You won't see many people riding these today! It was one of the early forms of bicycle. Is it called a: (a) Boneshaker? (b) Penny Farthing? (c) Tandem?

5—If you lift up a flat stone, you might find this fearsome-looking beetle. But don't be alarmed. It is harmless—and doesn't have a sting in its tail! Is it a: (a) Devil's Coach Horse? (b) Colorado Beetle? (c) Deathwatch Beetle?

PICS

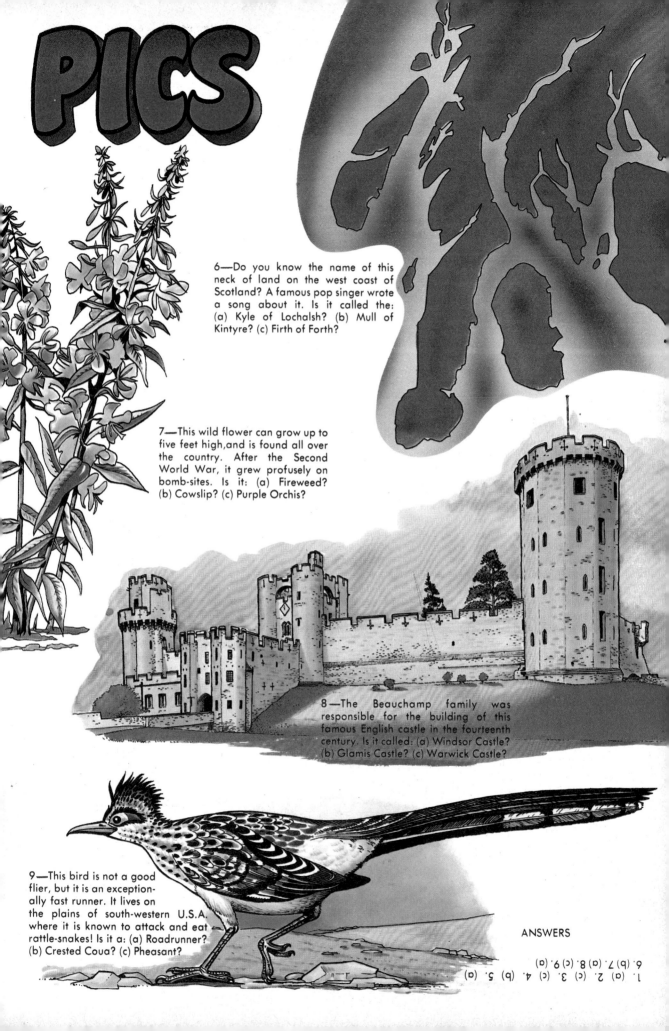

6—Do you know the name of this neck of land on the west coast of Scotland? A famous pop singer wrote a song about it. Is it called the: (a) Kyle of Lochalsh? (b) Mull of Kintyre? (c) Firth of Forth?

7—This wild flower can grow up to five feet high, and is found all over the country. After the Second World War, it grew profusely on bomb-sites. Is it: (a) Fireweed? (b) Cowslip? (c) Purple Orchis?

8—The Beauchamp family was responsible for the building of this famous English castle in the fourteenth century. Is it called: (a) Windsor Castle? (b) Glamis Castle? (c) Warwick Castle?

9—This bird is not a good flier, but it is an exceptionally fast runner. It lives on the plains of south-western U.S.A. where it is known to attack and eat rattle-snakes! Is it a: (a) Roadrunner? (b) Crested Coua? (c) Pheasant?

ANSWERS

6. (b) 7. (a) 8. (c) 9. (a)

1. (a) 2. (c) 3. (c) 4. (b) 5. (a)

Fatty shoots out of the tunnel and lands on the bedspring.

WAAH!

AAAA—

-AARGH!

Inside the hut—

OH, NO! HE'S LANDED IN THE PANTRY!

PANTRY

MUNCH! MUNCH!

GET HIM OUT BEFORE HE SCOFFS OUR GRUB!

GULP! I CAN'T. THE DOOR'S LOCKED AND I'VE LOST THE KEY!

YOU CLOT! WE CAN'T EVEN BURST THE DOOR OPEN!

HO-HO! I CAN EAT AS MUCH AS I WANT. THE BUNCH CAN'T GET IN TO STOP ME!

Meanwhile—

GRRR! COME BACK HERE!

STEADY ON, LADS! LOSING THE KEY WAS AN ACCIDENT!

A laughter treat when old pals meet!

The NUMSKULLS

I'VE BEEN INVITED TO A REUNION OF MY OLD SCHOOL PALS. I CAN HARDLY REMEMBER THEM.

I CAN HARDLY REMEMBER THEM!

MEMORY SCREEN

BRAIN DEPT.

I'LL JUST GIVE HIS MEMORY A JOG BY SHOWING A FEW PICTURES.

So—

FATTY FENWICK

SKINNY SIMPSON

SMILEY SMYTHE

CURLY DONALD

YES! IT'S ALL COMING BACK TO ME. I WONDER IF THEY'VE CHANGED AT ALL.

Then—

OH, NO! MY SUIT'S LIKE A DOG'S DINNER.

IT'LL BE ALL RIGHT IF HE GIVES IT A SPONGE AND A PRESS.

BRAIN DEPT.

MY SUIT'S LIKE A DOG'S DINNER!

GIVE IT A SPONGE AND A PRESS

SUGGESTION BOX

Then—

IT'S TAKEN QUITE A TIME TO DO THIS. I'LL HAVE TO HURRY.

But—

BAH! IT'S RAINING! I'LL TAKE MY BROLLY.

Fruit hoot!

A tale about cheese that's sure to please!

BEEFY DAN
THE FAST-FOOD MAN

THOSE HAMBURGERS SMELL GOOD, DAN.

I'M GLAD YOU LIKE 'EM, BOSS.

I'LL LEAVE THIS LOT HERE WHILE I FRY SOME MORE.

COO! GRUB! I'LL TELL THE OTHERS.

And—

YUM! I CAN'T WAIT TO GET STUCK INTO THIS LOT.

Soon—

I'M LOOKIN' FORWARD TO THIS BURGER.

Suddenly—

MUNCH! THIS IS DELICIOUS!

Then—

I HEAR SOMEONE SNORING.

IT'S COMING FROM YOUR HAMBURGER.

THAT'S FUNNY. IT'S STOPPED.

SMIFFY, COME IN AND CLEAR THE DINING TABLE FOR ME, PLEASE!

OKAY, MUM!

WASH YOUR HANDS BEFORE YOU TOUCH THE DISHES, SMIFFY!

I'M JUST ABOUT TO DO THAT, MUM.

YOU'RE NOT WASHING THEM IN THE KITCHEN SINK. I HAVE CLOTHES SOAKING IN THERE!

HUH! ALL RIGHT!

I'LL WASH MY HANDS IN THE BATHROOM SINK INSTEAD.

But—

OH, NO! THE DOOR'S LOCKED! ARE YOU IN THERE, DAD?

YES! SO GET LOST! I'M HAVING A BATH!

OUR SHERIFF'S AN APE!

COYOTE CREEK is normally a nice, quiet town in the Wild West for it has two sheriffs to keep the peace. One is a normal bloke called Danny Blain—but the other is Danny's pet, a huge ape called Charlie.

BE A BIT MORE CHOOSEY ABOUT YOUR STAFF, MISTER CREEDY. THAT'S THE SECOND TIME THIS WEEK THAT CHARLIE'S FOUND WANTED CRIMINALS WORKING FOR YOU!

BUT THOSE TWO ARE MY COOKS.

CROOKS, YOU MEAN! THEY'RE WANTED FOR ROBBERY.

JUST BE A BIT MORE CAREFUL OR I'LL CLOSE YOUR PLACE DOWN.

GRR! HIM AND THAT OVERGROWN MONKEY ARE GETTING TOO BIG FOR THEIR BOOTS.

Catching crooks is very hungry work and Charlie had only one thought on his mind as he patrolled the town later that day— food!

Suddenly, the huge ape's eyes opened wide. Someone had been dropping bananas.

YUM-YUM!

Charlie's long strides ate up the ground—and he ate up the bananas!

At last he came to the end of the trail.

In more ways than one! A blow on the head knocked him cold.

And when Charlie recovered he was frussed up like a turkey.

JUST YOU STAY THERE, YOU BIG APE.

HUH?

Some time later, Blinky Bradley was stumbling up a dark alley.

Suddenly—

IS THAT YOU, CHARLIE? WHAT HAVE YOU BEEN DOING IN THE BANK?

That's when Blinky found out the meaning of 'hard cash'! The hairy thief swung his bag of loot and Blinky went out like a light!

OW!

Meanwhile, Danny was getting a bit anxious about his pal.

I WONDER WHERE CHARLIE IS. IT'S NOT LIKE HIM TO BE LATE.

I'LL HAVE TO GO AND LOOK FOR HIM.

Then—

WOW! WHAT'S THIS? HEY! IT'S OLD BLINKY BRADLEY!

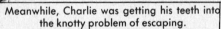

Now no one makes a monkey out of Charlie and gets away with it. He raced out of his prison shack, determined to find his attacker. Instead, he found the posse!

THERE'S THE BANK ROBBER NOW. ARREST HIM.

CHARLIE!

JUST HOLD IT RIGHT THERE, CHARLIE. I'LL HAVE TO PUT YOU IN JAIL UNTIL I GET TO THE BOTTOM OF THIS.

HUH?

Soon the hairy sheriff was locked up in a tiny cell.

NOW, DON'T CAUSE ANY TROUBLE. I'VE GOT A LOT OF INVESTIGATING TO DO.

Charlie was miserable. No one seemed to believe he was innocent.

As he stared out through the bars, Charlie suddenly caught sight of a man going into the hotel. And there was something very familiar about his shirt! The head-banger had worn a shirt just like it.

The huge ape was determined to catch the man and no cell was going to hold him back, so—

Then—

The angry sheriff stormed into the hotel. But then—

Charlie was as hard as iron, but he didn't fancy stopping any lead. He took to his heels.

With bullets whizzing round his ears, he leapt into the saddle of a horse hitched to a rail.

HUP!

Charlie gave a tug on the reins— and the whole rail came loose!

HE'S LET MY HORSE FREE. WHOA, TRIGGER!

In the confusion that followed, the jail-breaker made good his escape.

EEK!

OW!

WHAT HIT ME?

HELP!

WHOA!

Charlie headed for the hills. He was in big trouble and he needed time to think.

He also needed food. He searched in the saddlebags of the horse he had 'borrowed'.

That's when he found the bananas! He was just going to gobble them up when a thought struck him. They were the same kind as the ones that he had been following!

Charlie put two and two together and came up with a very painful answer.

The horse clearly belonged to the crook with the club, so Charlie slapped it with a banana skin and off it ran. The ape hoped it would lead him to the crook's hideout.

The horse headed straight back towards town. Charlie raced after it. He had to see where it finally stopped.

And that's when he got a shock. The nag pulled up outside Creedy's hotel!

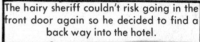

The hairy sheriff couldn't risk going in the front door again so he decided to find a back way into the hotel.

Then—

HO-HO! WE GOT THOUSANDS OF DOLLARS FROM THE BANK AND EVERYONE THINKS THAT CHARLIE DID IT, MISTER CREEDY.

THAT'S RIGHT, MICK—THANKS TO YOU CLOBBERING CHARLIE AND ME WEARING THIS APE SKIN!

HA-HA!

Charlie had seen enough. He shinned up a nearby tree.

He swung his powerful body up . . .

. . . and then down! Straight through the window.

AAGH!

AAIIEEE!

Danny Blair was searching for clues when he heard roars and squeals of pain.

SOMEBODY'S IN TROUBLE! LET'S GO.

GRR!
HELP!
OW!
GRR!
EEK!

Then Charlie came into view, dragging the two crooks behind him.

CHARLIE! YOU'VE GOT THE CASH FROM THE BANK! THOSE TWO MUST BE THE REAL ROBBERS.

When Danny found the ape skin he knew what had happened. Charlie was completely innocent! The bank manager was delighted to get his money back and—

HERE'S A LITTLE REWARD. YOU'LL BE ABLE TO BUY YOURSELF SOME BANANAS.

But Danny had other plans for the reward money.

SORRY, CHARLIE BUT YOU DAMAGED THE JAIL. THIS'LL HELP TO PAY FOR IT.

BAH!

Lots of mishaps with burglar traps!

Here's a silly billy! He thinks chili's chilly!

HUNGRY HOSS

'Water' hoot with the silly old coot!

COLONEL BLINK

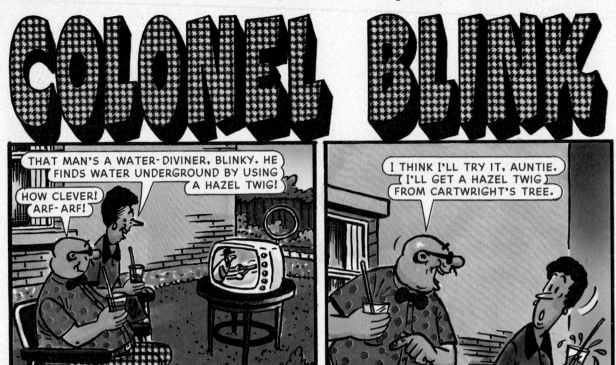

BEEZER

1—Ginger wants to take the lift to the toy department upstairs but he doesn't know which floor it's on because the names are jumbled up. Can you help him unscramble them?

REDHWARA — 1
TRIFUNERU — 2
INOTSETARY — 3
ARFOWTOE — 4
TRELELACI — 5
OYTS — 6

2—Mo and Mirabelle are admiring the table lamps. There is a design on each shade which changes in a certain pattern from left to right. See if you can work out what design should be on the fourth lamp.

3— Six little Numskulls are hidden on these pages. See if you can find them.

4—The Beezer artist has made 10 deliberate mistakes in drawing this Santa's Grotto. Can you spot them?

SANTA'S GROTTO

SNAKES & LADDERS

DRAUGHTS

TEEZERS

5—Dick and Harry are helping Pop look for the Menswear department. Turn 'Mens' into 'Wear' in four moves, changing one letter each time to form a new word.

MENS

WEAR

6—Blinky thinks these dummies all look the same, but only two are, in fact, identical. Which two?

1 2 3 4 5

7—The Bunch only have enough money for one pair of socks. Brainy thinks the one who has the fewest number of pairs should get the new socks. He has one pair less than Tiny who has two pairs more than Fatty. Dopey has one pair more than Lanky and two pairs less than Tiny. If Brainy has 5 pairs who should get the socks?

ANSWERS

1—Hardware, furniture, Stationery, Footwear; Electrical, Toys.

2— ☪ ▼ / ✴ ● / ✸ ○

3—Inside shade of table lamp on left side of table; In cab of toy lorry; At window of doll's house; Beside Pop's foot; Behind Blinky's legs; Between Tiny and Dopey.

4—Santa has one boot and one shoe; United kingdom is upside down on globe; Guard has rifle upside down; Doll has three legs; Door on doll's house is upstairs; Wrong number of squares on draught board; Computer spelled wrongly; Steering wheel in rear seat of car; Cowboy facing wrong way on horse; Sails wrong way round on yacht.

5—Mens—Tens—Teas—Tear—Wear, is one way of doing it.

6—3 and 5 are identical.

7—Lanky. He has the fewest pairs of socks.

Laughs for you with Saucy Sue!

Smiffy has a lucky break — and no mistake!

A tick-tock shock!

The sheriff of Happy Valley sleeps soundly.

ZZZ!

Suddenly—

BANG! BANG! BANG! BANG!

WHASSAT?

BAH! IT'S THE HILLYS AND THE BILLYS FEUDIN' AGAIN! IT'S THE SAME EVERY MORNING!

BANG! BANG!

Soon—

HEY! QUIT THIS FEUDIN'!

CLEAR OFF!

YEAH! WE'RE ENJOYING OURSELVES!

SHERIFF'S OFFICE

GRR! I'LL STOP THEM YET, DEPUTY.

Then—

HM! I'VE JUST HAD A GREAT IDEA!

So—

I'LL PUT MY CLOCK IN THIS CRATE!

You're sure to grin when the Bunch sleep in!

Minutes later—

After school—

Later—

Come dawn—

YOUR PLAN WORKED, BRAINY. WE'RE ALL AWAKE BRIGHT AND EARLY.

COCK-A-DOODLE-DO

RIGHT! LET'S GET UP AND DO OUR LINES!

Much writing later—

I'VE FINISHED! IT'S TIME FOR SCHOOL NOW!

LET'S GO!

And so—

MORNING, SIR! HERE ARE THE LINES YOU ASKED FOR!

WELL DONE, BOYS!

Later—

HO-HO! THE BUNCH WERE UP SO EARLY THAT THEY'VE FALLEN ASLEEP.

WAKEN UP, BOYS!

YAWN! IS IT TIME FOR SCHOOL ALREADY?

NO! IT'S TIME TO GO HOME!

GRR! TEACHER GAVE US MORE LINES TO DO BECAUSE WE FELL ASLEEP IN CLASS!

IT'S BRAINY'S FAULT! THAT COCKEREL WOKE US UP TOO EARLY!

The MUNCHERS

Down below—

COUGH! START DIGGING! I'VE AN IDEA.

Much digging later—

NOW LET'S HEAD FOR THE SURFACE.

And—

PERFECT! RIGHT UNDER FARMER'S WIFE'S WASHING.

Meanwhile—

HAR! THEM MUNCHERS SHOULD APPEAR ANY SECOND NOW.

But—

TAKE THAT, YOU FOOL!

BAM!

LOOK WHAT YOU'VE DONE! YOU'LL HAVE TO DO THE WASHING AGAIN!

NEE-HEE! FARMER'S PLANS TO CATCH US HAVE GONE UP IN SMOKE!

Peace and quiet turn into a riot!

The NUMSKULLS

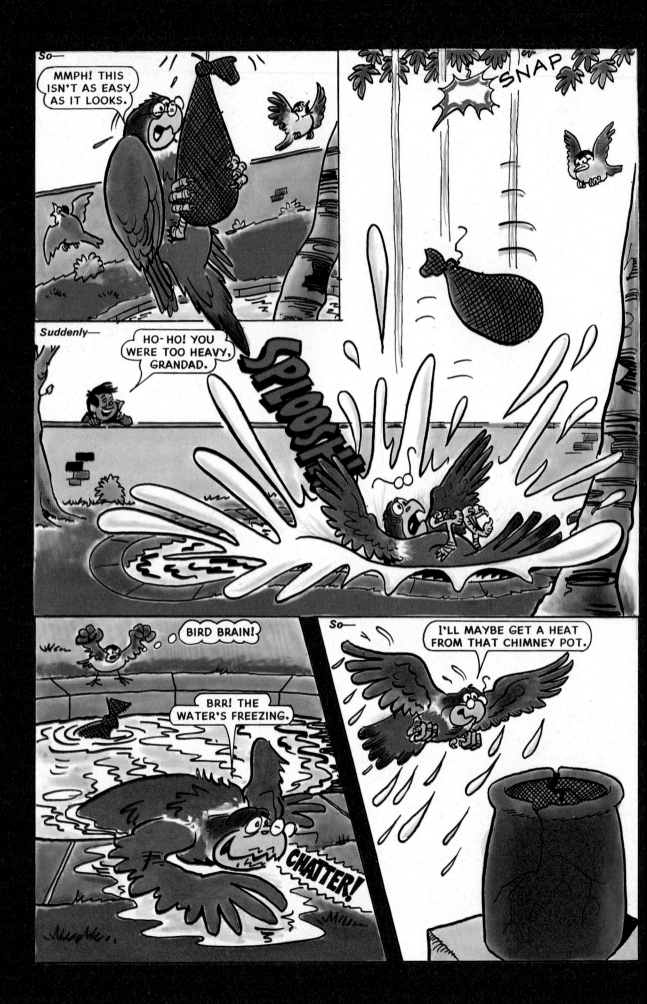

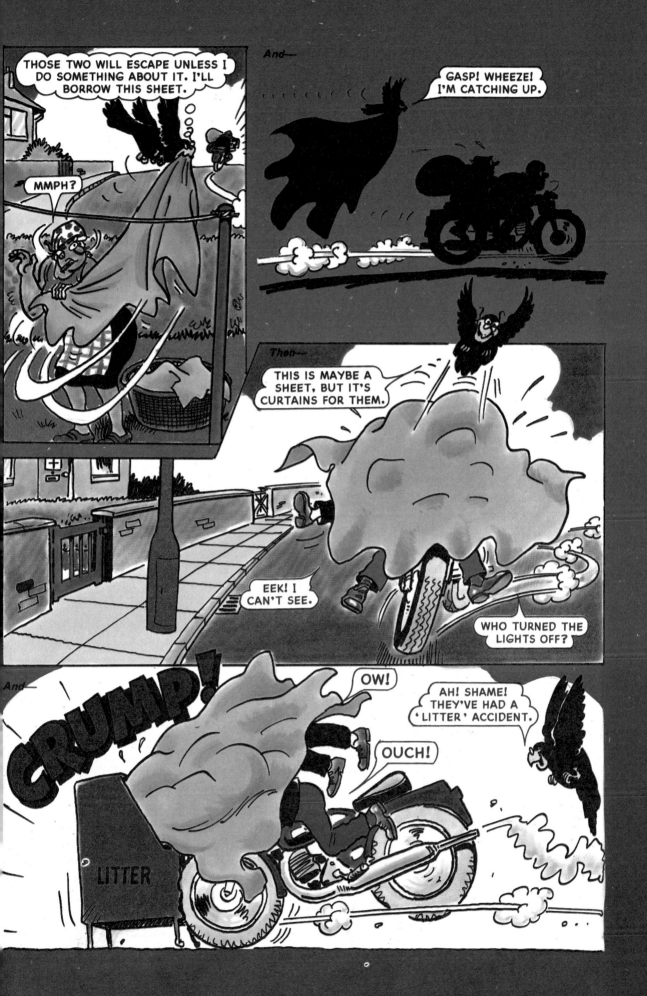

The Hillys are a mess but far from 'armless'!

Next morning—and everyone's asleep!

Well, almost everyone!

WE'RE GONNA FIX THOSE BLUNDERBUSSES!

SSH! QUIETLY DOES IT!

Later—

YAH! THE BILLYS ARE SOFTIES!

WHAT'S GOIN' ON?

GRR! GRAB THE BLUNDERBUSSES, MEN!

THE BILLYS ARE BONEHEADS!

BOO TO THE BILLYS

THEY DON'T SMELL TOO GOOD EITHER!

YAH! WE'RE NOT SCARED!

AIM!

THE BILLYS ARE BONEHEADS

BOO TO THE BILLYS

WE'LL VENTILATE YOU VARMINTS.

But—

HO-HO!

HA-HA!

BANG! BANG! BANG! BANG!

A laugh or two with you-know-who!

What do you think of Baby Blink?

Baby Crockett